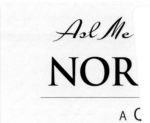

Ask Me...

NOR

A Q

G000146518

Compiled by Julia Skinner

THE FRANCIS FRITH COLLECTION

www.francisfrith.com

First published in the United Kingdom in 2011 by The Francis Frith Collection®

This edition published exclusively for Identity Books in 2011 ISBN 978-1-84589-556-3

British Library Cataloguing in Publication Data

Ask Me Another! Norfolk - A Quiz
Compiled by Julia Skinner

The Francis Frith Collection
Unit 6, Oakley Business Park,
Wylye Road, Dinton,
Wiltshire SP3 5EU
Tel: +44 (0) 1722 716 376
Email: info@francisfrith.co.uk
www.francisfrith.com

Printed and bound in England

Front Cover: **SHERINGHAM, FISHERMEN 1906** 56880p
Frontispiece: **THE SANDS 1899** 44482

The colour-tinting is for illustrative purposes only, and is not intended to be historically accurate

CONTENTS

QUESTIONS

ANSWERS

QUESTIONS

NORFOLK DIALECT WORDS

1. What does 'atwin' mean?

2. What is a 'bishy barney bee'?

3. What is a 'dodman'?

4. If you are 'duddering', what are you doing?

5. What is a 'harnser'?

6. What does it mean if you are 'luggy'?

7. What is a 'lummox'?

8. What would you be doing if you were having a 'mardle'?

9. What sort of bird is a 'mavish'?

10. You might find a 'mawkin' in a field – what is it?

11. What is a 'mawther'?

12. What is an 'uhmtie-tump'?

SPORT

13. Which Norfolk golf course was featured by the famous British golfer Tony Jacklin in a film of his favourite golf courses?

14. Norwich City Football Club is known as 'The Canaries', in reference to the canary rearing that the city is famous for. This nickname came into use in the early 1900s – by what name was the club previously known?

15. Norwich City FC maintains a fierce rivalry with its East Anglian neighbour Ipswich Town FC. When the two clubs meet, the occasion is called the 'the East Anglian Derby' but it is also known by a nickname – what is it?

16. Yarmouth has an important horse-racing course at Jellicoe Road with high quality racing attracting top trainers and jockeys. What is the name of the annual racing festival at the course that is a highlight in the local calendar?

17. Great Yarmouth Town Football Club, established in 1897, was one of the founder members of the Eastern Counties League in 1935. What is the club's nickname, and why?

18. A modern addition to Great Yarmouth's sporting facilities came in 2008, when a Grand Prix track was opened at the Pleasure Beach gardens – for which type of vehicle?

19. The King's Lynn Stars are the town's motorcycle speedway team – can you name the three other names by which the team has been known?

ARTS AND LITERATURE

20. What is the connection between Norfolk and a famous fictional black horse?

21. A work believed to be the first book written in English by a woman was produced in Norfolk, in Norwich, in the 14th century. What was this, and who wrote it?

22. The artist John Sell Cotman, born at Thorpe-next-Norwich in 1782, founded a famous school of artists with John Crome – what was it called, and what sort of paintings were its artists known for?

23. Cromer is mentioned as a bathing place in one of Jane Austen's novels – which one?

24. What is the connection between Norwich and the Beatles' album 'Sergeant Pepper's Lonely Hearts Club Band' of 1967?

THORPE ST ANDREW, RIVER YARE 1919 69075

COLTISHALL, A CORNFIELD 1902 48127

FOLKLORE, LEGENDS AND CUSTOMS

25. What is the connection between Norfolk and the pantomime story 'The Babes in the Wood'?

26. What is known as 'Old Shuck' in several villages of Norfolk, such as Coltishall, and why would you NOT want to see it?

27. The Church of All Saints at Upper Sheringham has some remarkable bench ends carved with various figures, one of which features a legendary watery lady – who was she?

28. Many Norfolk villages and towns feature delightful painted signs depicting significant people or events in the history of the place, either in fact or legend, or reflecting traditional trades. Who is the person depicted on the town sign for Swaffham, shown in photograph S237008, below?

SWAFFHAM, THE TOWN SIGN c1955 S237008

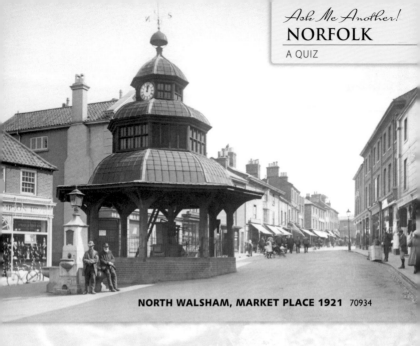

NORTH WALSHAM, MARKET PLACE 1921 70934

HISTORY AND ARCHAEOLOGY

29. What is the circular object at the top of the village sign for Snettisham, seen in photograph S464022 (right), and why is this object associated with Snettisham?

30. What is Grimes' Graves, seven miles north-west of Thetford?

31. The Church of St Nicholas at the coastal village of Blakeney, west of Sheringham, is unusual for having two towers – why?

32. When was the Battle of North Walsham, and who fought it?

33. Who were the 'Strangers' who came to Norwich in the 16th century?

34. The stone keep of Norwich Castle, seen in the background of photograph 28177 (opposite), is the largest in England apart from the Tower of London. Following a rebellion of Norfolk people in 1549, the rebel leader was captured and hanged from the keep of Norwich Castle – who was he, and how has he been remembered in Norwich?

35. Which medieval Norfolk family is famous for a series of letters and other correspondence between family members that is an invaluable source of information about life between the years 1422 and 1509?

36. Walsingham Priory in Norfolk was visited by more pilgrims in the Middle Ages than any other religious site in England, apart from Canterbury. What did they come to see?

37. What was known as a 'troll' in Great Yarmouth in the past, and where in the town can you still see one?

NORWICH, THE CATTLE MARKET AND THE CASTLE 1891
28177 (opposite page)

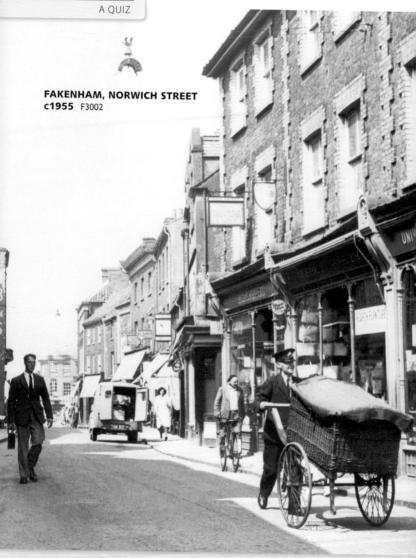

**FAKENHAM, NORWICH STREET
c1955** F3002

TRADE AND INDUSTRY

38. Fakenham has commemorated a former major industry of the area in its streets in an unusual way – what is it?

39. During the Middle Ages Norfolk prospered through the woollen and weaving trade, but this trade declined in the late 18th century as the Industrial Revolution gained pace. The newly-invented machinery for the textile mills needed to harness the power of fast-flowing water, but the slow-moving streams and rivers of Norfolk were unsuitable for this purpose and the textile trade moved to Yorkshire and Lancashire. However, during the heyday of Norfolk's woollen and weaving industry, a village in the county gave its name to fine cloth – which village was it?

40. What were 'swills', items that were unique to Great Yarmouth and the nearby Suffolk town of Lowestoft?

41. Norfolk is famous for the manufacture of which hot yellow condiment?

42. For several centuries shoemaking was an important local industry in Norwich. James Smith, who had a leather shop on the Market in Norwich, had a 'cunning scheme' in the 1790s which changed the nature of shoe manufacturing – what was it?

GENERAL KNOWLEDGE -NORFOLK

43. How did Rampant Horse Street in Norwich get its name?

44. Photograph 81810 (below) shows one of Norwich's landmarks, Samson and Hercules House at Tombland. It is named after the two figures which grace the front of the house. Which is Samson and which is Hercules?

45. What are 'wherries'?

NORWICH, SAMSON AND HERCULES HOUSE, TOMBLAND 1929 81810

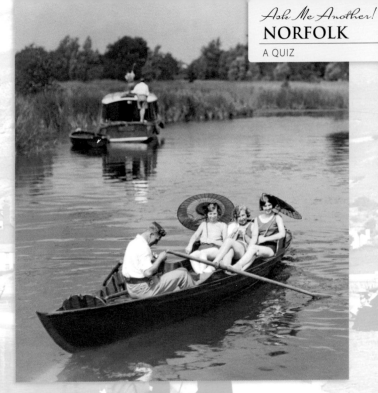

LUDHAM, BOATING ON WOMACK WATER c1930 L110035x

46. The Norfolk Broads have been a watery playground for holidaymakers for decades, but these broad expanses of water are actually man-made – how so?

47. A word commonly found in the Broadland area of Norfolk is a 'staithe' – what is this?

48. Which Broadland village is sometimes called 'little Venice'?

DOWNHAM MARKET, THE CLOCK TOWER 1952 D149009

49. What would you be doing in Norfolk if you were 'quanting'?

50. Wroxham (more correctly Hoveton) in the Norfolk Broads is famous as the home of what is claimed to be 'The World's Largest Village Store' – what is the name of the store?

51. A major long distance path crosses Norfolk, starting from Knettishall Heath Country Park in Suffolk and ending at Holme-next-the-Sea on the north Norfolk coast. What is it called?

52. Photograph D149009 (opposite) shows one of the landmarks of Downham Market, the cast-iron clock tower that was presented to the town in 1878 by James Scott, a local grocer and draper; this view shows the clock tower as it looked in 1952, it is now painted black and white. Downham Market was once famous for its horse fair, known as Winnold's Fair because it began on the feast of St Winnold in March. It was one of the largest horse fairs in the country, and its importance to Downham Market is recalled in the two horses on the town sign. Downham Market used to be nicknamed 'The Gingerbread Town' – why?

53. What is the unusual characteristic of many Norfolk churches?

54. When and why did Great Yarmouth become 'Great'?

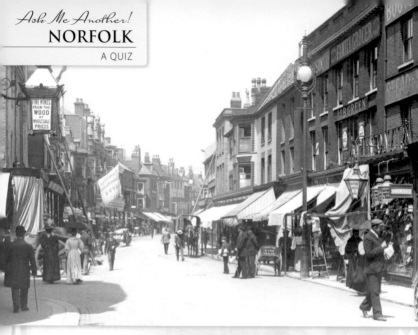

GREAT YARMOUTH, KING STREET 1896 37958

55. Which king is King Street in Great Yarmouth named after?

56. A structure believed to be the oldest civic building in England stands in Great Yarmouth – what is it?

57. Why might a sailor in the Royal Navy who was acting strangely be described as 'Going to Yarmouth' in the past?

58. The Hippodrome building in Great Yarmouth, on the junction of St Peter's Road and St George's Road, is one of only two surviving – what – in Britain?

59. In the High Street of Watton, near Thetford, is the unusual clock tower shown in photograph W383003 (below), surmounted by a weathervane depicting a hare and a barrel – why is this?

60. What sort of creature is a Norfolk Black?

61. A famous inhabitant of West Runton, near Cromer, died some 600,000 years ago, and its skeleton was found in the cliffs after erosion in the 1990s – what sort of creature was it?

WATTON
THE CLOCK TOWER
c1950 W383003

62. What is the raised building seen in Wymondham's market place on the right of photograph W159035 (below), and what was it used for?

63. Why are the men of Caister-on-Sea famous for not turning back?

64. St Edmund's Church in Acle, between Great Yarmouth and Norwich, is most unusual – why?

WYMONDHAM, THE MARKET PLACE AND THE CROSS c1965
W159035

65. What are 'Stookey Blues'?

66. King's Lynn was not always the name of the town.
    What was its original name?

67. The magnificent St Nicholas's Chapel in King's Lynn, just off
    Tuesday Market Place, has an unusual internal roof in its nave.
    What is this sort of roof called, and why?

68. This photograph shows the Tuesday Market Place in King's Lynn in the 1890s. The large stone building second from the right is the Corn Exchange, built in 1854. A statue of a woman stands at the top of its roof – who does it represent?

KING'S LYNN, TUESDAY MARKET PLACE 1898 40886

69. What relic of the Civil War of the 17th century can be seen suspended from the roof at the entrance to Hampton Court in Nelson Street in King's Lynn?

70. Why is there a road in King's Lynn named after the American president John F Kennedy?

71. Photograph D25100 (below) shows the famous town sign across the High Street at Dereham (also known as East Dereham). Who does it depict, and why?

DEREHAM, THE TOWN SIGN c1955 D25100

SHERINGHAM, FISHERMEN 1906 56880

72. By what nickname is a resident of Sheringham sometimes known?

73. By what nickname are the people of Holt known, and why?

74. One of the curiosities in Holt is the 'Pineapple Obelisk' which stands at Obelisk Plain at the end of the High Street. The obelisk is inscribed with mileage distances to Norfolk's principal towns – but why is this information inaccurate?

75. Inside the Church of Holy Trinity and All Saints at Winterton-on-Sea is an interesting memorial chapel – what is it, and why is it also very sad?

FAMOUS PEOPLE

76. Which Norfolk man became Britain's first Prime Minister?

77. The palatial Holkham Hall near Wells-next-the-Sea was built in the 18th century to a design by Palladio. The house and estate was inherited by Thomas William Coke (1754-1842), known to history as 'Coke of Norfolk' – what is he famous for?

78. One of Norfolk's most famous sons, Admiral Lord Nelson, was born at Burnham Thorpe near King's Lynn in 1758. Norfolk has an impressive monument to him somewhere on its coast – where is it?

NORWICH, NURSE CAVELL'S MEMORIAL 1929 81819

HEACHAM, THE VILLAGE SIGN c1965 H57119

79. Photograph 81819 (opposite) shows the memorial to the courageous local heroine Edith Cavell in Norwich, in its original (1918) position in the middle of Tombland (it has since been moved to a plot beside the Erpingham Gate of the cathedral precinct). For what is she commemorated?

80. The village sign for Heacham is shown in photograph H57119 (above) – who does it depict, and what is the link with Heacham?

81. During the Roman conquest of Britain in the first century AD, a famous fiery lady from the Norfolk area caused the invaders some problems. What was her name, and the name of the Celtic tribe she ruled?

CROMER, THE LIFEBOAT 1922 72651

82. What is the link between King's Lynn in Norfolk and Vancouver in Canada?

83. Norfolk's lifeboatmen are renowned for their courage. Photograph 72651 (above) shows the crew of the lifeboat 'Louisa Heartwell' at Cromer in 1922, displaying their medals for gallantry. The coxswain of the 'Louisa Heartwell' from 1909 to 1947 is famous as the most decorated lifeboatman in Britain – who was he?

84. What is the link between King Henry VIII (1491-1547) and Diss, a small town on the Norfolk/Suffolk border?

85. Which influential radical writer and political activist of the 18th century was born and educated in Thetford?

86. During the Napoleonic Wars a military garrison was based at South Denes at Great Yarmouth, and in the early 1800s the barrack master was Captain George Manby, born in Denver in Norfolk in 1765. In February 1807 he could only be a helpless onlooker when a ship ran aground in a storm just 60 yards offshore from Great Yarmouth, with the loss of over 200 lives. This tragic event inspired him to invent something which has since saved thousands of lives – what was it?

87. Where in the Norwich area can you find a statue of the Norwich Market character Billy Bluelight, and what was he famous for?

THETFORD, MARKET PLACE 1929 81830

ANSWERS

NORFOLK DIALECT WORDS

1. 'Atwin' means 'between'.

2. A 'bishy barney bee' is a ladybird.

3. A 'dodman' is a snail.

4. 'Duddering' means 'shivering'.

5. A 'harnser' is a heron.

6. If you are 'luggy', you are deaf.

7. A 'lummox' is a clumsy or awkward person.

8. If you were having a 'mardle', you would be having a gossip or a chat with someone.

9. A 'mavish' is a thrush.

10. A 'mawkin' is a scarecrow.

11. A 'mawther' is a young woman.

12. An 'uhmtie-tump' is a mole hill.

**NORWICH
RAMPANT HORSE
STREET 1891**
28163

COLMAN.

SPORT

13. The Royal Cromer Golf Course. It became a full 18-hole course in 1895, and the famous course designer Tom Morris was involved in advising the club. Tony Jacklin considers it to be one of the finest in the country, and he included it in a film of his favourite golf courses.

14. Norwich City Football Club was originally known as 'The Cits' (short for 'Citizens'), but the current nickname of 'The Canaries' seems to have come into use during the 1906-07 season. When City played in the new strip of yellow shirts for the first time in the following season, one local newspaper marked the event with the comment 'The Cits are dead, but the Canaries are very much alive'.

15. The 'East Anglian Derby' is also known as the 'Old Farm Derby', a joking reference to the name of the famous 'Old Firm Derby' played between Celtic and Rangers in Scotland.

16. The annual Eastern Festival, with 3 days of flat racing.

17. The nickname of Great Yarmouth Town Football Club is 'The Bloaters', after the famous Yarmouth bloaters (smoked herrings) produced in the town.

18. Great Yarmouth's Grand Prix track at the Pleasure Beach gardens is for Segways. A Segway is a two-wheeled electric vehicle on which the rider balances as the vehicle moves along. The vehicle is steered by the rider leaning forward, backwards, and left or right, whilst using a tall steering handlebar.

19. The King's Lynn Stars motorcycle speedway team has been known variously as The Knights, The Silver Machine and The Stars.

ARTS AND LITERATURE

20. The classic book 'Black Beauty', written by Anna Sewell, who was born in Great Yarmouth in 1820 in a house on Church Plain, and lived at Old Catton, now part of Norwich, from 1866 until her death in 1878. 'Black Beauty' was written to protest against cruelty to horses, and has sold around 40 million copies since it was published in 1877. Anna Sewell is remembered in Norwich in the name of Sewell Park, Sewell Road, and the Sewell Barn Theatre in the grounds of Sewell Park College.

21. One of the most important English religious mystics of the Middle Ages was Julian of Norwich, an anchoress (a female hermit living in a cell attached to the church, who engaged herself in contemplative prayer) at St Julian's Church on King Street. She produced a number of religious tracts, but her major work was 'Revelations of Divine Love' (or 'A Revelation of Love – in Sixteen Shewings'), believed to be the first book written in English by a woman. Julian became renowned as a spiritual authority, and her saying 'All shall be well and all shall be well and all manner of thing shall be well' is still one of the most famous lines in Catholic theological writing.

22. John Sell Cotman and John Crome founded the Norwich School of painters. Their subjects were typically landscapes, coasts and marine scenes from around Norwich and Norfolk, but rustic scenes were also popular, notable for a detailed and realistic observation of nature.

23. Cromer is mentioned in Jane Austen's 'Emma' (published in 1816), in which Emma's father Mr Woodhouse says of the resort: "You should have gone to Cromer, my dear, if you went anywhere. Perry was a week at Cromer once, and he holds it to be the best of all the sea-bathing places. A fine open sea, he says, and very pure air."

24. The reference to Pablo Fanque in the song 'Being for the Benefit of Mr Kite' on the album: 'The Hendersons will all be there, Late of Pablo Fanque's Fair…'. Pablo Fanque was a famous circus proprietor of the 19th century, but his real name was William Darby, born in Norwich and christened in All Saints' Church on 28 February 1796, and almost certainly the only Norwich-born person to feature in a Beatles' lyric! William Darby was the child of a mixed marriage – his father, John Darby, was a black man who worked as a butler. William became an orphan while young and was apprenticed to a circus, taking the name of Pablo Fanque. He eventually became the first black man in Britain to become the proprietor of a circus company. John Lennon wrote the song after seeing an old poster for Pablo Fanque's circus for sale in an antique shop.

**GREAT YARMOUTH, THE AMUSEMENT PARK
BRITANNIA PIER 1908** 60647

FOLKLORE, LEGENDS AND CUSTOMS

25. The story of 'The Babes in the Wood' is believed to be based on a true event which happened in the Wayland area near Watton in the 16th century, when two children were left orphaned. Their wicked uncle (said to have lived at Griston Hall) ordered his men to take the children into Wayland Wood and murder them, so he could claim their inheritance. However, the men could not bring themselves to kill the children but abandoned them in the wood, where they died. The ghosts of the children are said to haunt the wood, which was known as Wailing Wood in the past.

26. Several villages in Norfolk are said to be haunted by a large phantom black dog, known as 'Old Shuck'. A sighting of the hound presages death.

27. A bench end in the Church of All Saints at Upper Sheringham depicts a mermaid, which local legend says was modelled from life from a mermaid who would creep ashore from the beach to the north door of the church to listen to the congregation singing.

28. Swaffham's town sign depicts John Chapman, the 'Swaffham Pedlar', who legend says found two pots of gold coins buried in his garden after being guided to them in a dream. He is believed to have paid for much of the construction of the church of St Peter and St Paul in Swaffham and there is a delightful wooden carving of John Chapman on the prayer desk inside the church.

GORLESTON, THE HARBOUR 1894 33393

HISTORY AND ARCHAEOLOGY

29. It represents a Celtic torc, or neck ornament. A fabulous collection of more than a hundred gold, silver and electrum torcs, dating from the Iron Age, was found here, known as the Snettisham Hoard. They are now in Norwich Castle Museum.

30. Grimes' Graves is the name of an ancient flint mine from the late Neolithic and early Bronze Ages. Ancient man used Norfolk's rich flint deposits for making flint-knapped axes and other tools. Flint was mined here on a large scale over 5,000 years ago, and the pits, shafts and quarries of the prehistoric workings can still be seen. The Anglo-Saxons named them after their god Grim, calling them 'Grim's quarries', or 'the Devil's holes'.

31. Blakeney was a major port in medieval times, and the smaller tower of the church served as a mark for sailors heading for the port: it used to carry a beacon at night.

32. The Battle of North Walsham took place south of the town in 1381, and was one of the last engagements of the Peasants' Revolt. It was fought between the local rebels led by 'The King of the Commons', Geoffrey Litster, a dyer from the Norfolk village of Felmingham, and the forces of Henry le Despenser, Bishop of Norwich. The rebels were easily routed, and Litster was captured and hanged, drawn and quartered in the town.

33. The word 'Strangers' is used in Norwich to refer to Dutch and Walloon weavers who were invited to come to the city in the reign of Queen Elizabeth I to give a kick-start to the city's declining weaving trade. The first 30 'Strangers' came to Norwich in 1566. Of these craftsmen, 24 were Dutch and six were Walloons (a French-speaking people from the area now known as Belgium). Within five years over 4,000 of their countrymen had joined them in the city. These immigrants brought many things to the city, including banknotes, tulips and their favourite pet, the canary, a bird which has now become closely associated with the city. Over the years local breeders have established a specific type of these delightful little birds, known as the Norwich Canary.

34. In 1549 'Kett's Rebellion' broke out in Norfolk, an outburst of protest against enclosure of the common land by the poor and the lower middle class, led by Robert Kett of Wymondham. Several thousand people gathered on Mousehold Heath, but were attacked and dispersed by forces of the Earl of Warwick, and Robert Kett was captured and hanged from the keep of Norwich Castle. The city ordered that a local holiday be established celebrating Kett's downfall, and all the shops in the city were to close on 27th August 'from henceforward forever'! However, attitudes to the rebellion have changed over the centuries, and on the 400th anniversary of Kett's death a plaque was put up at Norwich Castle in his honour.

35. The Paston family. 'The Paston Letters' is the name of a unique collection of family correspondence that documents the rise and fall in fortunes of a Norfolk family during the turbulent 15th century and the Wars of the Roses period. Most of the letters and other documents are now in the British Library.

36. Pilgrims in the Middle Ages came to Walsingham to see the Holy House at Walsingham Priory, a miraculous re-creation of the house in Nazareth where Jesus Christ was brought up, together with other wonders including a healing well. The holy shrine of medieval times was destroyed during the Dissolution in 1538. In 1897 the 14th-century Slipper Chapel at Walsingham was re-established as a Roman Catholic shrine, the National Shrine of our Lady of Walsingham – it was called the Slipper Chapel because in medieval times this was where pilgrims would remove their shoes before walking barefoot for the last Holy Mile to the shrine of Our Lady at Walsingham – and in the 20th century an Anglican shrine of Our Lady of Walsingham was also established in the town. Walsingham is once again a place of peace to pilgrims who come to worship there.

37. In former centuries, before most of them were damaged by enemy bombing during the Second World War, huddled around the quay at Great Yarmouth were the famous and unique Rows, 156 parallel narrow alleyways between the Market Place and King Street on one side, and the Quays along the river on the other. The Rows developed in this way in medieval times, as a result of houses having to be crammed close together within the perimeter of the town walls. Special carts called 'trolls' were developed to negotiate the alleyways; they were long and narrow, with their wheels set beneath the body of the cart rather than the outside. There is a replica of a troll in the Market Place in Great Yarmouth.

TRADE AND INDUSTRY

38. The major industry of Fakenham in the 19th and 20th centuries was printing. This heritage is recalled with a number of printing blocks set into the surface of the town's market place.

39. The village of Worstead near North Walsham was once one of the main centres of the weaving industry which made Norfolk one of the wealthiest regions of medieval England, and gave its name to fine cloth.

40. For many centuries Great Yarmouth's main prosperity was based on herring fishing, and by the end of the 19th century it was the leading herring port in the world. 'Swills' were specially-made wicker baskets for herrings which were unique to Great Yarmouth and Lowestoft. Rows of 'swills' filled with fish can be seen in photograph G56503 (opposite) of Great Yarmouth's fish market c1900. By the 1960s fish stocks were seriously depleted and the town's herring fleet is no more, but Great Yarmouth's fishing heritage is commemorated in the Time and Tide museum on Blackfriar's Road, housed in a former herring smokery.

41. Mustard. Bright yellow fields of mustard have been grown in the county ever since Jeremiah Colman opened his first mustard mill near Norwich in 1814 and started making his condiment.

42. James Smith of Norwich is said to have been the first person in the world to think of selling boots and shoes in stock shoe sizes, rather than having each customer individually measured.

GREAT YARMOUTH, THE FISH MARKET c1900   G56503

GENERAL KNOWLEDGE - NORFOLK

43. Rampant Horse Street in Norwich was named after the Rampant Horse Inn, an old coaching inn which used to stand in the area, which was demolished in the closing years of the 19th century.

44. Samson is on the left-hand side of photograph 81810 on page 12, holding a lamb, and Hercules is on the right, with a lion's skin around his waist.

45. 'Wherries' are the flat-bottomed, broad-beamed boats with black sails that are often seen in old photographs of Norfolk life. Built of local oak, the gaff-rigged wherry was precisely designed for Broadland conditions – when sailing a wherry, you had to be able to sail very close to the wind, for the narrow waterways of the Broads allowed no extravagant tacking manoeuvres. The wherrymen were the prime movers in the past of grain, coal, timber, harvested reeds, crops and manufactured goods throughout Broadland and to the coastal ports. An example of a wherry is seen in photograph 48108, opposite.

46. In medieval times peat was dug in the Norfolk Broads area on a grand scale; the huge diggings were prone to flooding, and were inundated during periods of rising water levels, resulting in the landscape we know today.

47. 'Staithe' means a 'landing place'. It is the word used for all mooring places in the Broads, whether along a river or up an inlet.

48. The village of Horning has been called 'little Venice', or 'Venice in Broadland', because the cottages and houses which line the banks of the River Bure have lawns spreading down to the water's edge, with waterways like the canals of Venice running up into the gardens, many of which are linked by picturesque bridges.

HORNING, ON THE BROADS 1902 48108

49. 'Quanting' is a word used in Norfolk for the action of propelling a boat by means of a long pole. A man can be seen 'quanting' in photograph L110083, below.

50. 'Roys of Wroxham'. Alfred and Arnold Roy opened their store in Hoveton in 1899 and since then the business has expanded greatly. Hoveton is north of the River Bure, whilst Wroxham is south of the river, but the whole settlement is often referred to as Wroxham, hence 'Roys of Wroxham'. Roys Food Hall is shown as it looked c1940 in photograph H399113, opposite.

LUDHAM, 'QUANTING' BY THE WINDMILL c1955 L110083

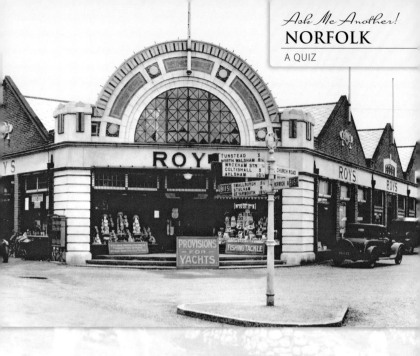

HOVETON, THE CROSS ROADS c1940 H399113

51. The Peddars Way. It follows the route of a Roman road. At Holme-next-the-Sea the Peddars Way meets another long distance footpath, the Norfolk Coast Path, which runs from Hunstanton to Cromer.

52. Downham Market was called 'The Gingerbread Town' in the past as many buildings in the town were constructed from the distinctive brown carrstone that was quarried locally.

BRADWELL, THE CHURCH
c1955 B496004

53. The distinguishing characteristic of many Norfolk churches is a round tower, often made of flint, of which 126 survive in the county. Photograph B496004 (opposite) of the church at Bradwell shows an example of such a round tower. These towers may reflect a shared culture across the North Sea – similar towers are found in Denmark and north Germany.

54. The earliest known document to call the town Great Yarmouth comes from the reign of Edward I (1272-1307). It was called Great Yarmouth to distinguish it from Little Yarmouth on the other side of the river, now known as Southtown, not to distinguish it (as many people think) from Yarmouth on the Isle of Wight.

55. King Street in Great Yarmouth is named after Charles II, who visited the town in 1671.

56. Photograph 28703 (below) shows the historic flint-built Tolhouse in Great Yarmouth. Built in the 13th century, it served as Great Yarmouth's town hall, court and gaol for 600 hundred years and is believed to be the oldest surviving civic building in England.

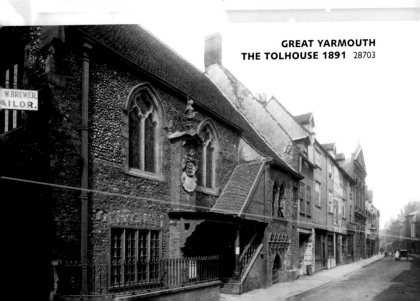

**GREAT YARMOUTH
THE TOLHOUSE 1891** 28703

57. In 1809 a Royal Naval Hospital was built on the Denes at Great Yarmouth for wounded sailors. Forty years later it became a hospital where sailors who were mentally ill were sent for treatment. Thus the phrase 'Going to Yarmouth' became naval slang for someone showing signs of mental strain.

58. The Hippodrome building in Great Yarmouth is one of only two custom-built, permanent circus buildings in Britain (the other one is in Blackpool). It was built in 1903 by George Gilbert, the famous circus showman.

59. The weathervane is a play on the name of Watton – it depicts a hare, for which the local name is a 'wat', and a barrel, a 'tun', giving 'Watton'. The hare and barrel motif also features on the coat of arms of Watton, which can also be seen on the clock tower above the clock.

60. A turkey. Norfolk is renowned for the quality of its poultry, and especially for its turkeys. In past centuries great flocks of Norfolk Black turkeys were driven on foot from Norfolk to London for the Christmas markets in great droves of 500 birds or more, a journey that took about 3 months.

61. In the 1990s the skeleton of a giant elephant was found in the cliffs at West Runton. It is the most complete such skeleton in the world, and is on display at Norwich Castle Museum.

62. The building is known as The Cross. It was built after a town fire of 1616 to replace the earlier building that stood on the site of the town's medieval market cross, marking the centre of Wymondham's market place in the Middle Ages. The open-sided area beneath the building was used as a shelter for people at the market, and the upper floor was where the market administration took place. In later years the upper storey of the building was used as the town meeting room.

63. In the cemetery of Holy Trinity Church at Caister-on-Sea is a memorial which commemorates the deaths of nine crewmen in a great storm when the Caister lifeboat 'Beauchamp' capsized on 14th November 1901 whilst on a rescue mission. At the enquiry afterwards, the coxswain James Haylett was asked why the lifeboat crew had carried on with their mission when conditions made a rescue impossible, and he answered: "They would never give up the ship. If they had to keep at it 'til now, they would have sailed about until daylight to help her. Going back is against the rules when we see distress signals like that." His response was reported by journalists as the phrase "Caister men never turn back", which was later adopted in the form "Never Turn Back" as a motto of the RNLI.

64. St Edmund's Church at Acle is unusual because it has a thatched nave roof and an octagonal top to its round tower (see photograph A204083, below).

ACLE, ST EDMUND'S CHURCH c1955 A204083

47

65. Named after the River Stiff, the Norfolk village of Stiffkey is famous for its 'Stookey (or Stewkey) Blues' – blue-shelled Norfolk cockles.

66. Founded by Herbert, Bishop of Norwich, around 1100, King's Lynn was known as Bishop's Lynn until it passed from the Church to the Crown during the reign of Henry VIII.

67. An 'angel roof', which dates from c1400 and is much earlier than other examples in the country, which are associated with tiered hammerbeam roofs and carvings from the period 1480 to 1520. The angels featured on the roof of St Nicholas's Chapel are on projecting struts over each window head; all are depicted full length with spread wings, and are unconnected to the roof. Each angel is different, with many either holding or playing a musical instrument.

68. Ceres, the Roman goddess of agriculture, grain, harvest and plenty.

69. King's Lynn was held for the Royalist cause in the Civil War, and in 1643 the town was besieged for almost three weeks by Parliamentarian forces. During the siege a 16lb cannonball went through a west window of St Margaret's Church and damaged a pillar. The cannonball can now be seen suspended from the roof at the entrance to Hampton Court in Nelson Street in the town.

70. Because an American firm, Dow Agro-chemicals, opened a plant in the town just after Kennedy had been elected President in 1960.

71. The sign commemorates St Withburga, a Saxon princess who is believed to have founded a nunnery here in AD654. The sign features two deer because, according to legend, two deer provided St Withburga with milk which she used to feed the workmen who were building her church until it was completed.

72. A 'Shannock' is the nickname for a resident of Sheringham, although some people say that to be a true 'Shannock' you must have parents and grandparents born in the town. It may originally have been a disparaging term given to the local fishermen by their arch-rivals from Cromer, possibly deriving from the dialect word 'shanny', meaning 'unruly'.

73. Holt people are known as 'Holt Owls' because of a local legend that at some time in the past an owl in the town made such a noise at night that it was disturbing everyone's sleep. Many efforts were made to catch the owl and remove it, but they were unsuccessful and the owl eluded capture every time. There are a number of references to owls all around the town, including an image of the Holt Owl on the town sign.

74. The Pineapple Obelisk is inscribed with the mileage to Norfolk's principal towns from Melton Constable Hall where it originally served as a gatepost – but incorrect information for the distances from Holt where it stands now!

75. Inside the church is a fishermen's memorial chapel which is made and decorated with wood from locally-wrecked ships. It is dedicated to fishermen who were lost at sea. Winterton Ness, an area of foreshore north of the village, is one of the most dangerous points along the English coast, and many ships have been lost here over the centuries. The author Daniel Defoe (1660-1731) recorded that in a single night in 1692 over 200 ships and 1,000 lives were lost off the coast here in a terrible storm.

FAMOUS PEOPLE

76. Sir Robert Walpole (1676-1745), who became Britain's first Prime Minister in 1721; he was also the MP for King's Lynn for 40 years. He was born at Houghton Hall in west Norfolk in 1676, and was referred to by both his friends and enemies as 'the fat old Squire of Norfolk' because of his Norfolk roots and down-to-earth ways.

77. Thomas William Coke, the great agriculturist known as 'Coke of Norfolk', is famous for his pioneering methods of agriculture, animal husbandry and livestock breeding. He is recognised as one of the instigators of the Agricultural Revolution in Britain.

78. After Lord Nelson's death at the Battle of Trafalgar in 1805, Great Yarmouth was chosen as the place for a Norfolk memorial to him, sited on the coast in the South Denes. The lofty monument is usually known as the Nelson Monument, but its correct name is the Norfolk Naval Pillar, although it has also been called the Britannia Monument, after the figure of Britannia that stands on the top. A local legend about the Nelson Monument is that the architect jumped to his death from the top in despair when he realised that the figure of Britannia was facing the 'wrong' way, looking inland rather than out to sea, but in fact Britannia was designed to look in this direction, and is looking towards Burnham Thorpe, Nelson's birthplace on the north Norfolk coast. On each side of the base of the monument are carved the names of the ships in which Vice-Admiral Lord Nelson achieved his most famous naval victories, above which are carved the names of the naval battles in which they were engaged. Inside the monument is a spiral staircase leading up to a viewing platform at the top of the column. The life and achievements of Lord Nelson are also celebrated in the Norfolk Nelson Museum on South Quay in Great Yarmouth, which holds a large collection of his letters, keepsakes, paintings, and medals.

79. Edith Cavell was born in Swardeston near Norwich in 1875. She became a nurse, and went to work in a hospital in Brussels in Belgium, but was on a visit to her mother in College Road when the First World War began in August 1914. Despite this, Edith returned to her work in Brussels and stayed on when the Germans occupied the city. She helped many Allied soldiers escape from Belgium, and for this she was shot by a German firing squad on 12th October 1915. Her body was returned to England after the war, and she is buried beside Norwich Cathedral.

80. Heacham's sign depicts the Native American princess Pocahontas, who is famous for saving the life of Captain John Smith during the early settlement of Virginia in America by throwing herself over his body to prevent him being killed by her father's warriors. In 1614 Pocahontas married another Virginian settler, John Rolfe (1585-1622), who was originally from Heacham Hall in Norfolk. John Rolfe brought his wife and their baby son back to England for a visit in 1616, and the family stayed at Heacham Hall for a time. Pocahontas was presented at court to King James I, and the depiction of her in Jacobean fashion on the sign was taken from an oil painting based on a woodcutting of her that was done at that time. Pocahontas fell ill and died on a ship anchored off Gravesend in Kent in 1617 as the family was about to return to Virginia, and was buried there, but an alabaster memorial to her was erected in St Mary's Church in Heacham in 1933.

81. The Victorians called her Boadicea, but she is now known as Boudica (or Boudicca), queen of the Iceni tribe, whose territory covered the area of what is now Norfolk. She led a rising against the Romans around AD60, and her forces sacked and burned the Roman towns of Camulodunum (Colchester), Verulamium (St Albans) and London before being defeated. The capital of the Iceni was called by the Romans 'Venta Icenorum', meaning 'the market town of the Iceni', which was just outside the modern-day village of Caister St Edmund near Norwich. It is now known as Caistor Roman Town.

82. Vancouver in Canada was named after Captain George Vancouver RN of King's Lynn, who undertook surveying voyages of the Pacific northwest coast. He was sent by the Admiralty to prepare navigation charts, from the Columbia river to Alaska, mainly in 1793-95. A statue of Captain Vancouver was erected in his hometown in 2000, beside the beautiful 18th-century Custom House where his father John Jasper Vancouver was Deputy Collector (see photograph K28717, opposite).

83. Henry Blogg, the coxswain of the 'Louisa Heartwell' from 1909 to 1947, was the most decorated lifeboatman in Britain, earning three gold and four silver medals, the George Cross and the British Empire medal for his bravery.

84. Diss was the birthplace (c1460) of John Skelton, poet laureate and tutor to Henry VIII when he was Prince of Wales; he is depicted teaching the young prince on the town sign. In later life John Skelton also served as the rector at Diss, from 1504 until his death in 1529.

85. Thomas Paine, author of the influential book 'The Rights of Man' and a participant in both the American and French revolutions, was born in Thetford in 1737 and educated at the Free Grammar School in the town. He emigrated to America in 1774 where he advocated the colony's bid for independence from Great Britain in a widely read pamphlet called 'Common Sense' (1776). He moved to France in the early stages of the French Revolution and wrote 'The Rights of Man' in its defence, but in later years he was unimpressed by Napoleon, describing him as 'the completest charlatan that ever existed', and he returned to America before his death in 1809. He is recognised as one of the Founding Fathers of the USA.

KING'S LYNN, CUSTOM HOUSE 2003 K28717

86. Amongst other nautical life-saving devices, Captain George Manby invented the breeches buoy, a rope-based device used to rescue people from shipwrecks. It is deployed either from land to ship or from ship to ship – a rope or line is fired across to the stranded ship, and people are then winched to safety along the line, attached to a sling or harness.

87. 'Billy Bluelight' was the nickname of a well-known character from Norwich Market in the past, whose real name was William Cullum. In summer he sold flowers on the Walk for a penny a bunch. He sold hot chestnuts in autumn, cough remedies in the winter and matches, which was probably the origin of his nickname of 'Billy Bluelight'. He was also famous for racing the 'Jenny Lind', a tourist boat, along the river between Bramerton and Norwich in the 1920s and 30s. He died in 1949 and is commemorated with a statue of him racing along on the Wherryman's Way at Bramerton, as well as a plaque on a seat on the river walk, in front of the railway station.

FRANCIS FRITH

PIONEER VICTORIAN PHOTOGRAPHER

Francis Frith, founder of the world-famous photographic archive, was a complex and multi-talented man. A devout Quaker and a highly successful Victorian businessman, he was philosophical by nature and pioneering in outlook. By 1855 he had already established a wholesale grocery business in Liverpool, and sold it for the astonishing sum of £200,000, which is the equivalent today of over £15,000,000. Now in his thirties, and captivated by the new science of photography, Frith set out on a series of pioneering journeys up the Nile and to the Near East.

INTRIGUE AND EXPLORATION

He was the first photographer to venture beyond the sixth cataract of the Nile. Africa was still the mysterious 'Dark Continent', and Stanley and Livingstone's historic meeting was a decade into the future. The conditions for picture taking confound belief. He laboured for hours in his wicker dark-room in the sweltering heat of the desert, while the volatile chemicals fizzed dangerously in their trays. Back in London he exhibited his photographs and was 'rapturously cheered' by members of the Royal Society. His reputation as a photographer was made overnight.

VENTURE OF A LIFE-TIME

By the 1870s the railways had threaded their way across the country, and Bank Holidays and half-day Saturdays had been made obligatory by Act of Parliament. All of a sudden the working man and his family were able to enjoy days out, take holidays, and see a little more of the world.

With typical business acumen, Francis Frith foresaw that these new tourists would enjoy having souvenirs to commemorate their days out. For the next thirty years he travelled the country by train and by pony and trap, producing fine photographs of seaside resorts and beauty spots that were keenly bought by millions of Victorians. These prints were painstakingly pasted into family albums and pored over during the dark nights of winter, rekindling precious memories of summer excursions. Frith's studio was soon supplying retail shops all over the country, and by 1890 F Frith & Co had become the greatest specialist photographic publishing company in the world, with over 2,000 sales outlets, and pioneered the picture postcard.

FRANCIS FRITH'S LEGACY

Francis Frith had died in 1898 at his villa in Cannes, his great project still growing. By 1970 the archive he created contained over a third of a million pictures showing 7,000 British towns and villages.

Frith's legacy to us today is of immense significance and value, for the magnificent archive of evocative photographs he created provides a unique record of change in the cities, towns and villages throughout Britain over a century and more. Frith and his fellow studio photographers revisited locations many times down the years to update their views, compiling for us an enthralling and colourful pageant of British life and character.

We are fortunate that Frith was dedicated to recording the minutiae of everyday life. For it is this sheer wealth of visual data, the painstaking chronicle of changes in dress, transport, street layouts, buildings, housing and landscape that captivates us so much today, offering us a powerful link with the past and with the lives of our ancestors.

Computers have now made it possible for Frith's many thousands of images to be accessed almost instantly. The archive offers every one of us an opportunity to examine the places where we and our families have lived and worked down the years. Its images, depicting our shared past, are now bringing pleasure and enlightenment to millions around the world a century and more after his death.

For further information visit: www.francisfrith.com

INTERIOR DECORATION

Frith's photographs can be seen framed and as giant wall murals in thousands of pubs, restaurants, hotels, banks, retail stores and other public buildings throughout Britain. These provide interesting and attractive décor, generating strong local interest and acting as a powerful reminder of gentler days in our increasingly busy and frenetic world.

FRITH PRODUCTS

All Frith photographs are available as prints and posters in a variety of different sizes and styles. In the UK we also offer a range of other gift and stationery products illustrated with Frith photographs, although many of these are not available for delivery outside the UK – see our web site for more information on the products available for delivery in your country.

THE INTERNET

Over 100,000 photographs of Britain can be viewed and purchased on the Frith web site. The web site also includes memories and reminiscences contributed by our customers, who have personal knowledge of localities and of the people and properties depicted in Frith photographs. If you wish to learn more about a specific town or village you may find these reminiscences fascinating to browse. Why not add your own comments if you think they would be of interest to others? See **www.francisfrith.com**

PLEASE HELP US BRING FRITH'S PHOTOGRAPHS TO LIFE

Our authors do their best to recount the history of the places they write about. They give insights into how particular towns and villages developed, they describe the architecture of streets and buildings, and they discuss the lives of famous people who lived there. But however knowledgeable our authors are, the story they tell is necessarily incomplete.